Puree diet Cookbook for Adults

A Complete Guide for Easy & Nourishing Meals, Delicious Dysphagia-Friendly Recipes | 30-Day Meal Plans

Dr. LAUREL GARNER

Table of Contents

Introduction

I've always been a passionate foodie, relishing the opportunity to explore new cuisines and experiment with flavors. But life took an unexpected turn when I was diagnosed with Dysphagia, a condition that made it difficult for me to swallow solid foods. The vibrant world of culinary delights suddenly seemed out of reach, replaced by a bland and monotonous diet of pureed foods.

Initially, I felt disheartened, mourning the loss of my favorite dishes and the satisfaction of a hearty meal. But as I delved deeper into the world of pureed cuisine, I discovered a hidden gem – a realm of culinary possibilities waiting to be unveiled.

With a newfound enthusiasm, I embarked on a mission to transform the pureed diet from a necessity into a culinary adventure. I spent countless hours in the kitchen, experimenting with different ingredients and techniques, determined to create dishes that were not only nutritious but also flavorful and satisfying.

Through trial and error, I discovered that the pureed diet offered a unique canvas for culinary creativity. By breaking down traditional ingredients into their purest form, I was able to create new and exciting flavor combinations that challenged my taste buds and sparked my imagination.

Along my journey, I also realized that the pureed diet was more than just a way to eat – it was a philosophy that embraced simplicity, mindfulness, and appreciation for the fundamental elements of taste and texture. It taught me to slow down, savor each bite, and find joy in the simplest of ingredients.

As my culinary skills evolved, I began sharing my recipes with friends and family, who were amazed at the transformation of their bland pureed meals into gourmet delights. Their encouragement fueled my passion, and I decided to compile my recipes into a cookbook, hoping to inspire others to embrace the pureed diet and rediscover the joy of eating.

This cookbook is a culmination of my culinary journey, a testament to the transformative power of food and the resilience of the human spirit. I hope that within these pages, you will find not just recipes but also a newfound appreciation for the pureed diet and its potential to bring joy, nourishment, and culinary satisfaction to your life.

Let's go on a food adventure together! We'll try different mashed up foods and discover all the yummy flavors and textures they have. We can turn eating mushy food into a fun and tasty experience.

Chapter 2

What is the Pureed Diet?

The pureed diet is a sort of mechanical soft diet that entails ingesting meals that have been blended or mashed until they are smooth and simple to swallow. This diet is commonly prescribed for patients who have difficulties chewing or swallowing due to diseases such as dysphagia, stroke, or head and neck cancer.

Who Needs to Follow a Pureed Diet?

A pureed diet may be recommended for those with the following conditions:

Dysphagia: Dysphagia is a swallowing problem that makes it difficult or risky to swallow solid meals or liquids. This may be caused by a multitude of conditions, including neurological diseases, muscular weakness, or anatomical abnormalities in the mouth, throat, or esophagus.

Stroke: A stroke may impair brain areas that govern swallowing, resulting in dysphagia.

Head and neck cancer: Surgery or radiation treatment for head and neck cancer might damage tissues involved in swallowing, requiring a pureed diet.

Dental difficulties: Severe dental disorders, such as loose or missing teeth, may make eating difficult, requiring a pureed diet.

Esophageal problems: Esophageal abnormalities, such as strictures or tumors, may make it difficult for food to pass down the esophagus, necessitating a pureed diet.

Other disorders: Certain neurological illnesses, such as Parkinson's disease or multiple sclerosis, might impede swallowing, requiring a pureed diet.

Benefits of the Pureed Diet

There are many benefits to adopting a pureed diet, including:

Reduced risk of aspiration: Aspiration occurs when food or liquids enter the trachea or lungs instead of the esophagus, increasing the risk of pneumonia. A pureed meal minimizes the risk of aspiration by making it simpler to swallow and manage food in the mouth.

Improved nutrition: A pureed diet may give appropriate nutrition when properly planned and supplemented with liquids and high-calorie items.

Reduced discomfort and suffering: Individuals with dysphagia typically feel discomfort and agony while swallowing solid meals. A pureed meal reduces this pain and enables simpler and more pleasurable eating.

Enhanced safety: For those with severe dysphagia, a pureed meal may help avoid choking or other consequences linked with swallowing difficulties.

The pureed diet can be a safe, healthy, and fun way to consume for persons with trouble chewing or swallowing. With careful preparation and a bit of ingenuity, you can prepare tasty and gratifying meals that match your dietary requirements and tastes.

Pureed Oatmeal with Berries and Nuts

Prep Time: 5 minutes
Cooking Time: 10 minutes
Servings: 2

Ingredients:

- 1 cup rolled oats
- 2 cups milk (dairy or plant-based)
- 1 cup mixed berries (strawberries, blueberries, raspberries)
- 1/4 cup mixed nuts (walnuts, almonds, or your preference)

Instructions:

1. In a saucepan, bring the milk to a mild boil.
2. Stir in the rolled oats and decrease heat to a simmer. Cook for 5-7 minutes until oats are mushy.
3. Take it away from heat and allow it cool down slightly.
4. Transfer the oats, berries, and nuts to a blender. Blend until smooth.
5. Pour into dishes and serve warm. Optionally, top with more berries and almonds.

Nutritional Value: (Per Serving)

- *Calories: 320*
- *Protein: 12g*
- *Carbohydrates: 45g*
- *Fat: 11g*
- *Fiber: 7g*

Pureed Scrambled Eggs with Cheese

Prep Time: 2 minutes
Cooking Time: 5 minutes
Servings: 1

Ingredients:

- 2 eggs
- 1/4 cup shredded cheese

Instructions:

1. Crack the eggs into a bowl and beat them until fully mixed.

2. Heat up a special pan that doesn't let the eggs stick to it. Put the eggs that have been mixed together into the pan.
3. Stir continually until the eggs start to set.
4. Sprinkle shredded cheese over the eggs and continue stirring until the cheese melts and the eggs are cooked to your preferred consistency.
5. Let it cool somewhat, then transfer to a blender and purée until smooth.
6. Serve warm.

Nutritional Value: (Whole Recipe)

- *Calories: 320*
- *Protein: 23g*
- *Carbohydrates: 2g*
- *Fat: 24g*
- *Fiber: 0g*

Pureed Yogurt Parfait

Prep Time: 5 minutes
Servings: 1

Ingredients:

- 1 cup plain yogurt
- 1/4 cup granola
- 1/2 cup mixed fruits (berries, sliced bananas, etc.)

Instructions:

1. In a blender, purée the plain yogurt until smooth.
2. Take a glass and layer pureed yogurt, granola, and mixed fruits alternately.
3. Keep adding layers one on top of the other until the glass is completely full.
4. Serve immediately for a refreshing breakfast.

Nutritional Value: (Whole Recipe)

- *Calories: 350*
- *Protein: 14g*
- *Carbohydrates: 60g*
- *Fat: 7g*

Smoothie

Prep Time: 5 minutes
Servings: 2

Ingredients:

- 1 cup spinach
- 1 ripe banana
- 1/2 cup mixed berries (strawberries, blueberries, raspberries)
- 1/2 cup plain yogurt
- One cup of almond milk (or your choice of milk)
- 1 tablespoon honey (optional)

Instructions:

1. Combine all items in a blender.
2. Blend until smooth and creamy.
3. Adjust the consistency by adding additional milk if required.
4. Pour into glasses and enjoy immediately.

Nutritional Value: (Per Serving)

Calories: 150

Protein: 5g

Carbohydrates: 30g

Fat: 3g

Fiber: 5g

Pureed Breakfast Bars

Prep Time: Varies dependent on selected bars
Servings: 1

Ingredients:

- **2 soft breakfast bars (of your choice)**
- **1/2 cup milk or yogurt (optional)**

Instructions:

1. Select soft breakfast bars appropriate for combining.
2. Cut the bars into smaller pieces.
3. Place the bar pieces into a blender.
4. Add milk or yogurt if required for appropriate consistency.
5. Blend everything together until it becomes a smooth liquid and then pour it into a cup.
6. Enjoy a drinkable breakfast!

Pureed Avocado Toast

Prep Time: 5 minutes
Cooking Time: 5 minutes
Servings: 2

Ingredients:

- 1 ripe avocado
- 4 slices whole-grain bread
- Salt, pepper, red pepper flakes (to taste)

Instructions:

1. Scoop out the avocado flesh into a bowl and mash it until smooth.
2. Toast the pieces of bread till golden brown.

3. Spread the pureed avocado on the toasted bread pieces.
4. Put a little bit of salt, pepper, and red pepper flakes on it until it tastes how you like it.
5. Serve immediately.

Nutritional Value: (Per Serving)

Calories: 220

Protein: 6g

Carbohydrates: 25g

Fat: 12g

Fiber: 10g

Pureed Potato Pancakes

Prep Time: 15 minutes

Cooking Time: 15 minutes

Servings: 4

Ingredients:

- 2 cups mashed potatoes
- 2 eggs

- 1/4 cup flour
- Salt and pepper to taste

Instructions:

1. In a bowl, mix mashed potatoes, eggs, flour, salt, and pepper until thoroughly blended.
2. Heat a non-stick pan over medium heat and add a little quantity of oil.
3. Scoop parts of the potato mixture onto the pan and flatten to make pancakes.
4. Cook the food for about 3 to 4 minutes on one side, then flip it over and cook it for another 3 to 4 minutes until it turns a nice golden color.
5. Let the pancakes cool slightly, then purée them in a blender until smooth.
6. Serve warm with chosen toppings.

Nutritional Value: (Per Serving)

- *Calories: 180*
- *Protein: 6g*
- *Carbohydrates: 28g*
- *Fat: 5g*
- *Fiber: 3g*

Pureed Mashed Sweet Potatoes

| **Prep Time:** *10 minutes* |
| **Cooking Time:** *25 minutes* |
| **Servings:** *4* |

Ingredients:

- 2 big sweet potatoes, peeled and cubed
- 2 tablespoons butter (or olive oil for a healthy choice)
- Salt and pepper to taste

Instructions:

1. Boil or simmer the sweet potatoes until tender.
2. Drain and mash them with butter (or olive oil), salt, and pepper until smooth.
3. Let it cool somewhat, then purée in a blender for a smoother consistency.
4. Serve simply or with your favorite toppings.

Nutritional Value: (Per Serving)

Calories: 150

Protein: 2g

Carbohydrates: 26g

Fat: 5g

Fiber: 4g

Pureed Pumpkin Pancakes

Prep Time: 15 minutes
Cooking Time: 15 minutes
Servings: 4

Ingredients:

- 1 cup pureed pumpkin
- 1 1/2 cups all-purpose flour
- 2 tablespoons sugar
- 1 tablespoon baking powder
- 1 teaspoon cinnamon
- 1/2 teaspoon nutmeg

- 1 cup milk
- 2 eggs
- 2 teaspoons melted butter

Instructions:

1. In a bowl, combine flour, sugar, baking powder, cinnamon, and nutmeg.
2. In another dish, stir together pumpkin puree, milk, eggs, and melted butter.
3. Combine the wet and dry ingredients until barely combined.
4. Heat a pan over medium heat and pour batter into the pan.
5. Cook until bubbles appear on the surface, then turn and cook until golden brown.
6. Let pancakes cool slightly, then purée in a blender until smooth.
7. Serve with favorite toppings.

Nutritional Value: (Per Serving)

- *Calories: 220*
- *Protein: 6g*
- *Carbohydrates: 35g*
- *Fat: 7g*
- *Fiber: 3g*

Pureed Carrot Muffins

| Prep Time: 15 minutes |
| Cooking Time: 20 minutes |
| Servings: 12 muffins |

Ingredients:

- 1 1/2 cups all-purpose flour
- 1 teaspoon baking powder
- 1/2 teaspoon baking soda
- 1/2 teaspoon salt
- 1 teaspoon cinnamon
- 1/2 cup melted butter
- 1/2 cup brown sugar
- 2 big eggs
- 1 cup pureed carrots
- 1/2 cup yogurt
- 1 teaspoon vanilla extract

Instructions:

1. Preheat oven to 350°F (175°C) and fill a muffin tray with liners.
2. Cook until bubbles appear on the surface, then turn and cook until golden brown.
3. In another dish, mix melted butter and brown sugar. Add eggs, pureed carrots,

yogurt, and vanilla extract. Mix thoroughly.

4. Gradually add dry ingredients to wet components and stir until just mixed.
5. Pour batter into muffin cups and bake for 18-20 minutes or until a toothpick inserted comes out clean.
6. Let muffins cool, then purée in a blender until smooth if desired.
7. Serve simple or with toppings.

Nutritional Value: (Per Muffin)

- *Calories: 180*
- *Protein: 3g*
- *Carbohydrates: 25g*
- *Fat: 8g*
- *Fiber: 1g*

Pureed Carrot Soup with Grilled Cheese

Prep Time: 10 minutes
Cooking Time: 30 minutes
Servings: 4

Ingredients:

- 1-pound carrots, chopped 1 onion, chopped 2 stalks celery, chopped 4 cups vegetable broth
- Salt and pepper to taste
- 8 slices bread

- Cheese slices
- Butter for grilling

Instructions:

1. In a saucepan, mix carrots, onion, celery, and vegetable broth. Simmer until veggies are tender.
2. Blend the cooked veggies till smooth. Season with salt and pepper.
3. Spread butter on bread pieces, add cheese, and cook until golden.
4. Serve the pureed soup with grilled cheese sandwiches.

Nutritional Value: (Per Serving - Soup)

- **Calories: 120**
- **Protein: 3g**
- **Carbohydrates: 25g**
- **Fat: 1g**
- **Fiber: 6g**

Pureed Chicken Salad Sandwich

Prep Time: 15 minutes
Servings: 2

Ingredients:

- 1 cup cooked chicken, pureed
- 2 tablespoons mayonnaise
- 2 tablespoons chopped celery
- 2 teaspoons chopped onion
- Bread or crackers for serving

Instructions:

1. Mix pureed chicken with mayonnaise, celery, and onion.

2. Spread the chicken salad over toast or crackers to create sandwiches.

Nutritional Value: (Whole Recipe)

- *Calories: 320*
- *Protein: 20g*
- *Carbohydrates: 6g*
- *Fat: 24g*
- *Fiber: 1g*
-

Pureed Tuna Noodle Salad

Prep Time: 20 minutes
Servings: 4

Ingredients:

- 1 cup cooked noodles, pureed
- 1 cup pureed tuna
- 2 tablespoons mayonnaise
- 2 tablespoons chopped celery
- 2 teaspoons chopped onion
- Lettuce or bread for serving

Instructions:

1. Mix pureed noodles, tuna, mayonnaise, celery, and onion.
2. Serve on lettuce leaves or as a sandwich filler.

Nutritional Value: (Whole Recipe)

- **Calories: 280**
- **Protein: 18g**
- **Carbohydrates: 18g**
- **Fat: 14g**
- **Fiber: 1g**

Pureed Vegetable Soup

- **Prep Time: 15 minutes**
- **Cooking Time: 25 minutes**
- **Servings: 6**

Ingredients:

- 2 cups chopped mixed veggies (carrots, celery, onions, potatoes)
- 4 cups vegetable broth
- Salt and pepper to taste
- Yogurt or sour cream for garnish (optional)

Instructions:

1. In a saucepan, add chopped veggies and vegetable broth. Simmer until veggies are soft.
2. Puree the cooked veggies and broth until smooth. Season with salt and pepper.
3. Serve hot, perhaps topped with a dollop of yogurt or sour cream.

Nutritional Value: (Per Serving)

- **Calories: 80**
- **Protein: 2g**
- **Carbohydrates: 18g**
- **Fat: 0.5g**
- **Fiber: 3g**

Pureed Pasta Salad

Prep Time: 20 minutes
Cooking Time: 10 minutes
Servings: 4

Ingredients:

- 2 cups cooked pasta, pureed
- 1 cup pureed veggies (such as tomatoes, bell peppers, cucumbers)
- 4 tablespoons dressing of choice

Instructions:

1. Mix pureed spaghetti and veggies with your preferred dressing.
2. Chill in the refrigerator before serving.

Nutritional Value: (Whole Recipe)

- **Calories: 300**
- **Protein: 6g**
- **Carbohydrates: 60g**
- **Fat: 2g**
- **Fiber: 5g**

Pureed Beef Stew

Prep Time: 20 minutes
Cooking Time: 1 hour 30 minutes
Servings: 6

Ingredients:

- 1-pound beef, cooked and pureed
- 2 cups chopped carrots and potatoes
- 1 cup diced onions
- 4 cups beef broth
- Salt and pepper to taste

Instructions:

1. In a saucepan, mix pureed meat, carrots, potatoes, onions, and beef broth. Simmer until veggies are soft.
2. Puree the prepared stew until smooth. Season with salt and pepper.
3. Serve hot.

Nutritional Value: (Per Serving)

- *Calories: 250*
- *Protein: 20g*
- *Carbohydrates: 15g*
- *Fat: 10g*

- *Fiber: 3g*

Pureed Salmon with Rice

Prep Time: 15 minutes
Cooking Time: 20 minutes
Servings: 4

Ingredients:

- 1 cup cooked salmon, pureed
- 2 cups cooked rice
- 1 cup pureed mixed veggies

Instructions:

1. Combine pureed salmon, boiled rice, and pureed veggies.
2. Serve the combination as a pureed meal.

Nutritional Value: (Whole Recipe)

- *Calories: 400*
- *Protein: 25g*
- *Carbohydrates: 45g*
- *Fat: 12g*
- *Fiber: 4g*

Pureed Chicken Stir-Fry

Prep Time: 20 minutes
Cooking Time: 15 minutes
Servings: 4

Ingredients:

- 2 cups cooked chicken, pureed
- 2 cups mixed veggies, boiled and pureed
- Stir-fry sauce of choice

Instructions:

1. Stir-fry pureed chicken and veggies with your choice of sauce.
2. Serve as a pureed meal.

Nutritional Value: (Whole Recipe)

- *Calories: 320*
- *Protein: 28g*
- *Carbohydrates: 20g*
- *Fat: 12g*
- *Fiber: 5g*

Pureed Lentil Soup

Prep Time: 15 minutes
Cooking Time: 40 minutes
Servings: 6

Ingredients:

- 1 cup dry lentils, rinsed
- 1 onion, chopped
- 2 carrots, chopped
- 4 cups vegetable or chicken broth
- Salt and pepper to taste

Instructions:

1. In a saucepan, add lentils, onion, carrots, and broth. Simmer until lentils are soft.
2. Puree the cooked soup until smooth. Season with salt and pepper.
3. Serve hot, perhaps served with yogurt or sour cream.

Nutritional Value: (Per Serving)

- *Calories: 180*
- *Protein: 12g*
- *Carbohydrates: 30g*
- *Fat: 1g*
- *Fiber: 12g*

Pureed Meatloaf

| Prep Time: 15 minutes |
| Cooking Time: 1 hour |
| Servings: 8 |

Ingredients:

- 1-pound ground beef, boiled and pureed
- 1 cup oats
- 1 egg
- 1/2 cup chopped veggies (onions, carrots)
- Tomato sauce for topping

Instructions:

1. Mix pureed meat, oats, eggs, and chopped veggies. Form into a loaf.
2. Bake in the oven until cooked through.
3. Puree the cooked meatloaf till smooth before serving.

Nutritional Value: (Per Serving)

- **Calories: 220**
- **Protein: 15g**
- **Carbohydrates: 15g**
- **Fat: 10g**
- **Fiber: 2g**

Pureed Creamy Tomato Soup with Grilled Cheese

Prep Time: 10 minutes
Cooking Time: 30 minutes
Servings: 4

Ingredients:

- 1 can (28 oz) pureed tomatoes
- 1 onion, chopped
- 2 cloves garlic, minced
- 1 cup heavy cream
- Salt and pepper to taste
- Bread slices
- Cheese slices
- Butter for grilling

Instructions:

1. In a saucepan, sauté onions and garlic until tender. Add pureed tomatoes and simmer for 20 minutes.
2. Stir in heavy cream, salt, and pepper. Simmer for a further 5 minutes.

3. Blend the soup until smooth using an immersion blender or a normal blender.
4. Spread butter on bread pieces, add cheese, and cook until golden.
5. Serve the creamy tomato soup with grilled cheese sandwiches.

Nutritional Value: (Per Serving - Soup)

- *Calories: 320*
- *Protein: 5g*
- *Carbohydrates: 20g*
- *Fat: 25g*
- *Fiber: 4g*

Pureed Salmon with Roasted Vegetables

Prep Time: 15 minutes
Cooking Time: 20 minutes
Servings: 2

Ingredients:

- 2 salmon fillets, roasted and pureed
- Assorted roasted veggies (bell peppers, zucchini, etc.)

- Olive oil
- Salt and pepper to taste

Instructions:

1. Roast salmon fillets and different veggies with olive oil, salt, and pepper.
2. Puree the roasted salmon until smooth.
3. Serve the pureed salmon with roasted veggies.

Nutritional Value: (Whole Recipe)

- *Calories: 400*
- *Protein: 40g*
- *Carbohydrates: 20g*
- *Fat: 18g*
- *Fiber: 6g*

Pureed Chicken and Vegetable Curry

| Prep Time: 20 minutes |
| Cooking Time: 30 minutes |
| Servings: 4 |

Ingredients:

- 2 cups pureed cooked chicken
- Assorted pureed veggies (bell peppers, peas, etc.)
- 2 teaspoons curry powder
- 1 cup coconut milk
- Salt and pepper to taste

Instructions:

1. In a skillet, add pureed chicken, veggies, curry powder, and coconut milk. Simmer till heated through.
2. Season with salt and pepper.
3. Serve the pureed chicken and vegetable curry over rice or naan bread.

Nutritional Value: (Whole Recipe)

- *Calories: 600*
- *Protein: 40g*

- *Carbohydrates: 30g*
- *Fat: 35g*
- *Fiber: 8g*

Pureed Butternut Squash Soup with Apple

Prep Time: 15 minutes
Cooking Time: 40 minutes
Servings: 6

Ingredients:

- 1 butternut squash, peeled and chopped
- 1 apple, peeled and diced
- 1 onion, chopped
- 4 cups vegetable broth
- 1/2 cup plain yogurt or cream (optional)
- Salt and pepper to taste

Instructions:

1. In a saucepan, simmer butternut squash, apple, onion, and vegetable broth until soft.
2. Puree the cooked ingredients until smooth. Add yogurt or cream if desired.
3. Season with salt and pepper.

4. Serve the pureed butternut squash soup with a dollop of yogurt or cream.

Nutritional Value: (Per Serving)

- *Calories: 120*
- *Protein: 2g*
- *Carbohydrates: 25g*
- *Fat: 1g*
- *Fiber: 5g*

Pureed Chicken Noodle Soup

Prep Time: 15 minutes
Cooking Time: 30 minutes
Servings: 4

Ingredients:

- 2 cups pureed cooked chicken
- 1 cup cooked noodles, pureed
- Assorted pureed veggies (carrots, celery, etc.)
- 4 cups chicken broth
- Parmesan cheese for topping

Instructions:

1. In a saucepan, add pureed chicken, noodles, veggies, and chicken broth. Simmer till heated through.

2. Serve the pureed chicken noodle soup topped with a sprinkling of Parmesan cheese.

Nutritional Value: (Whole Recipe)

- *Calories: 400*
- *Protein: 30g*
- *Carbohydrates: 40g*
- *Fat: 10g*
- *Fiber: 6g*

Pureed Shepherd's Pie

| Prep Time: 20 minutes |
| Cooking Time: 1 hour |
| Servings: 6 |

Ingredients:

- 1-pound ground lamb or beef, boiled and pureed
- Assorted pureed veggies (peas, carrots, etc.)
- Mashed potatoes
- Gravy for serving

Instructions:

1. Layer pureed meat and veggies in a baking tray.
2. Top with mashed potatoes.
3. Bake till heated thoroughly.
4. Serve the pureed Shepherd's Pie with a dab of gravy.

Nutritional Value: (Per Serving)

- *Calories: 350*
- *Protein: 25g*
- *Carbohydrates: 30g*

- *Fat: 15g*
- *Fiber: 5g*

Pureed Lentil Stew with Lemon

Prep Time: 15 minutes
Cooking Time: 40 minutes
Servings: 6

Ingredients:

- 2 cups pureed lentils
- Assorted pureed veggies (onions, carrots, etc.)
- 4 cups vegetable or chicken broth
- Juice of 1 lemon
- Salt and pepper to taste

Instructions:

1. In a saucepan, add pureed lentils, veggies, and broth. Simmer until flavors mingle.
2. Squeeze in lemon juice and season with salt and pepper.
3. Serve the pureed lentil stew with a squeeze of lemon juice.

Nutritional Value: (Per Serving)

- *Calories: 250*
- *Protein: 18g*
- *Carbohydrates: 40g*
- *Fat: 2g*
- *Fiber: 15g*

Pureed Salmon and Sweet Potato Mash

Prep Time: 20 minutes
Cooking Time: 30 minutes
Servings: 4

Ingredients:

- 2 cups pureed cooked salmon
- 2 cups mashed sweet potatoes
- 1/2 teaspoon cinnamon
- Chopped nuts for garnish

Instructions:

1. Mix pureed salmon with mashed sweet potatoes and cinnamon.
2. Serve the pureed salmon and sweet potato mash topped with chopped nuts.

Nutritional Value: (Whole Recipe)

- *Calories: 450*
- *Protein: 30g*
- *Carbohydrates: 30g*
- *Fat: 20g*
- *Fiber: 6g*

Pureed Chicken and Rice Casserole

| Prep Time: 15 minutes |
| Cooking Time: 45 minutes |
| Servings: 6 |

Ingredients:

- 2 cups pureed cooked chicken

- 2 cups cooked rice, pureed
- Assorted pureed veggies (peas, carrots, etc.)
- 1 cup creamy sauce (milk-based)
- Steamed broccoli or carrots for serving

Instructions:

1. Mix pureed chicken, rice, veggies, and creamy sauce.
2. Spread the mixture in a casserole dish and bake until cooked through.
3. Serve the pureed chicken and rice dish with steamed broccoli or carrots.

Nutritional Value: (Per Serving)

- *Calories: 300*
- *Protein: 20g*
- *Carbohydrates: 35g*
- *Fat: 10g*
- *Fiber: 4g*

Pureed Vegetable Fajitas

| Prep Time: 20 minutes |
| Cooking Time: 15 minutes |
| Servings: 4 |

Ingredients:

- Assorted pureed veggies (bell peppers, onions, etc.)
- Seasoned pureed beans
- Sour cream for serving
- Warm tortillas

Instructions:

1. Sauté pureed veggies till tender.
2. Heat-seasoned pureed beans.
3. Serve the pureed veggies and beans in warm tortillas with a dollop of sour cream.

Nutritional Value: (Whole Recipe)

- *Calories: 320*
- *Protein: 12g*
- *Carbohydrates: 50g*
- *Fat: 8g*
- *Fiber: 12g*

Chapter 6: Snacks

Pureed Yogurt with Fruit and Granola

| Prep Time: 5 minutes |
| Servings: 1 |

Ingredients:

- 1/2 cup plain yogurt
- Assorted fruits (berries, banana slices)
- 1/4 cup granola

Instructions:

1. Puree the plain yogurt and fruits together until smooth.
2. Top the pureed mixture with granola for extra texture.

Nutritional Value:

- *Calories: 250*
- *Protein: 8g*
- *Carbohydrates: 40g*
- *Fat: 6g*
- *Fiber: 5g*

Pureed Avocado Toast

| Prep Time: 5 minutes |
| Servings: 1 |

Ingredients:

- 1 ripe avocado
- Slices of whole-grain bread
- Salt and pepper to taste

Instructions:

1. Puree the ripe avocado till smooth.
2. Spread the pureed avocado over toasted whole-grain bread pieces.
3. Season with salt and pepper to taste.

Nutritional Value:

- *Calories: 180*
- *Protein: 3g*
- *Carbohydrates: 12g*
- *Fat: 15g*
- *Fiber: 7g*

Smoothie

| Prep Time: 5 minutes |
| Servings: 1 |

Ingredients:

- Assorted fruits (banana, berries, mango)
- Handful of spinach
- 1/2 cup yogurt
- 1/2 cup milk or almond milk

Instructions:

1. Blend all items together until smooth.
2. Adjust consistency by adding additional liquid if required.

Pureed Sweet Potato Fries

| Prep Time: 10 minutes |
| Cooking Time: 25 minutes |
| Servings: 4 |

Ingredients:

1. 2 big sweet potatoes, peeled and cut into fries
2. 2 tablespoons olive oil
3. Salt, pepper, paprika (to taste)

Instructions:

1. Preheat oven to 425°F (220°C). Toss sweet potato fries with olive oil and seasonings.
2. Bake in the oven for 20-25 minutes until it gets crispy and is fully cooked inside.
3. Puree the roasted sweet potato fries till smooth.

Nutritional Value:

- *Calories: 150 (per serving)*
- *Protein: 2g*
- *Carbohydrates: 25g*
- *Fat: 6g*
- *Fiber: 4g*

Pureed Applesauce

Prep Time: 10 minutes
Cooking Time: 15 minutes
Servings: 4

Ingredients:

- 4 apples, peeled, cored, and cut
- 1/2 cup water
- Cinnamon (optional)

Instructions:

1. Cook apples and water in a saucepan until soft.
2. Blend the cooked apples till smooth.
3. Optionally, add cinnamon for taste.

Nutritional Value:

- *Calories: 60 (per serving)*
- *Protein: 0g*
- *Carbohydrates: 15g*
- *Fat: 0g*
- *Fiber: 3g*

Pureed Mashed Potatoes

Prep Time: 15 minutes
Cooking Time: 20 minutes
Servings: 4

Ingredients:

- 4 medium-sized potatoes, peeled and chopped
- 1/4 cup milk (or non-dairy substitute)
- 2 tablespoons butter (or olive oil)
- Salt and pepper to taste

Instructions:

1. Boil diced potatoes until soft, then drain.
2. Mash the potatoes with milk, butter (or olive oil), salt, and pepper until smooth.
3. Puree the mashed potatoes for a smoother consistency if desired.

Nutritional Value:

- *Calories: 150 (per serving)*
- *Protein: 3g*
- *Carbohydrates: 30g*
- *Fat: 2g*
- *Fiber: 3g*

Pureed Hummus with Pita Bread

| Prep Time: 10 minutes |
| Servings: 4 |

Ingredients:

- One can (15 ounce) of chickpeas (garbanzo beans), drained
- 2 tablespoons tahini
- 2 tablespoons olive oil
- 1 garlic clove, minced
- Juice of 1 lemon
- Salt to taste
- Pita bread for serving

Instructions:

1. Blend chickpeas, tahini, olive oil, garlic, lemon juice, and salt until smooth.
2. Serve the pureed hummus with pita bread for dipping.

Nutritional Value:

- *Calories: 180 (per serving)*

- *Protein: 6g*
- *Carbohydrates: 20g*
- *Fat: 9g*
- *Fiber: 6g*

Pureed Carrot Sticks with Peanut Butter

Prep Time: 5 minutes
Servings: 2

Ingredients:

- Carrot sticks
- Peanut butter

Instructions:

1. Puree the carrot sticks till smooth or purchase pre-made pureed carrot sticks.
2. Dip or spread the carrot puree with peanut butter for a tasty snack.

Pureed Rice Cakes with Apple Butter

Prep Time: 5 minutes
Servings: Varies

Ingredients:

- Rice cakes
- Apple butter

Instructions:

1. Spread apple butter over rice cakes for a tasty and healthful snack.

Pureed Cottage Cheese with Fruit

Prep Time: 5 minutes
Servings: 1

Ingredients:

- Cottage cheese
- Assorted fruits (berries, sliced peaches, etc.)

Instructions:

1. Puree the cottage cheese and fruits until smooth.

Enjoy the creamy pureed cottage cheese with assorted fruits.

Chapter 7: Deserts

Pureed Fruit Parfait

Prep Time: 5 minutes
Servings: 1

Ingredients:

- 1/2 cup pureed yogurt
- 1/4 cup granola
- Assorted pureed fruits (strawberries, bananas, blueberries)

Instructions:

1. Layer pureed yogurt, granola, and pureed fruits in a glass.
2. Repeat layers as desired.

Pureed Mango Mousse

Prep Time: 15 minutes
Servings: 4

Ingredients:

- 2 ripe mangoes, pureed
- 1 cup plain yogurt
- 2 tablespoons honey

Instructions:

1. Blend pureed mangoes, yogurt, and honey until smooth.
2. Chill the mixture for a couple of hours before serving.

Nutritional Value:

- *Calories: 120 (per serving)*
- *Protein: 3g*
- *Carbohydrates: 28g*
- *Fat: 1g*
- *Fiber: 2g*

Pureed Chocolate Avocado Pudding

- Prep Time: 10 minutes
- Servings: 2

Ingredients:

- 1 ripe avocado, pureed
- 2 teaspoons cocoa powder
- 2 tablespoons honey

Instructions:

1. Blend avocado, cocoa powder, and honey until smooth.
2. Chill for an hour before serving.

Nutritional Value:

- *Calories: 180 (per serving)*
- *Protein: 3g*
- *Carbohydrates: 17g*
- *Fat: 13g*
- *Fiber: 6g*

Pureed Pumpkin Cheesecake

Prep Time: 20 minutes
Cooking Time: 1 hour
Servings: 8

Ingredients:

- 1 cup pureed pumpkin
- 8 oz cream cheese, softened
- 1/2 cup sugar
- Spices (cinnamon, nutmeg, cloves)

Instructions:

1. Beat cream cheese, sugar, pumpkin, and spices until smooth.
2. Bake in a pie crust at 350°F (175°C) for 50-60 minutes.

Nutritional Value:

- *Calories: 250 (per serving)*
- *Protein: 4g*
- *Carbohydrates: 22g*
- *Fat: 16g*
- *Fiber: 2g*

Pureed Sweet Potato Pie

Prep Time: 15 minutes
Cooking Time: 1 hour
Servings: 8

Ingredients:

- 2 cups pureed sweet potatoes
- 2 eggs
- 1/2 cup sugar
- Spices (cinnamon, nutmeg)

Instructions:

1. Mix pureed sweet potatoes, eggs, sugar, and spices until smooth.
2. Bake in a pie crust at 350°F (175°C) for 50-60 minutes.

Nutritional Value:

- *Calories: 220 (per serving)*
- *Protein: 4g*
- *Carbohydrates: 34g*
- *Fat: 8g*
- *Fiber: 3g*

Pureed Peach Cobbler

| Prep Time: 15 minutes |
| Cooking Time: 40 minutes |
| Servings: 6 |

Ingredients:

- 2 cups pureed peaches
- 1 cup oats
- 1/4 cup brown sugar
- Spices (cinnamon, nutmeg)

Instructions:

1. Mix pureed peaches, oats, sugar, and spices.
2. Bake at a really hot temperature of 375°F (190°C) for about 35 to 40 minutes, until it turns a nice golden brown color.

Nutritional Value:

- *Calories: 180 (per serving)*
- *Protein: 4g*
- *Carbohydrates: 40g*
- *Fat: 2g*
- *Fiber: 5g*

Pureed Apple Crisp

Prep Time: 15 minutes
Cooking Time: 45 minutes
Servings: 6

Ingredients:

- 4 cups pureed apples
- 1 cup oats
- 1/4 cup honey
- Spices (cinnamon, nutmeg)

Instructions:

1. Mix pureed apples, oats, honey, and spices.
2. Bake at 350°F (175°C) for 40-45 minutes until bubbling.

Nutritional Value:

- *Calories: 220 (per serving)*
- *Protein: 2g*
- *Carbohydrates: 50g*
- *Fat: 2g*
- *Fiber: 6g*

Pureed Pear Fritters

Prep Time: 20 minutes
Cooking Time: 15 minutes
Servings: 4

Ingredients:

- 2 cups pureed pears
- 1 cup flour
- 2 eggs
- Oil for frying

Instructions:

1. Mix pureed pears, flour, and eggs till a batter forms.
2. Fry a dollop of batter in heated oil till golden brown.

Nutritional Value:

- *Calories: 180 (per serving)*
- *Protein: 5g*
- *Carbohydrates: 30g*
- *Fat: 4g*
- *Fiber: 3g*

Pureed Banana Bread

Prep Time: 15 minutes
Cooking Time: 1 hour
Servings: 10

Ingredients:

- 4 ripe bananas, pureed
- 1/2 cup butter (or oil)
- 1 cup sugar
- 2 eggs
- 2 cups flour

Instructions:

1. Mix pureed bananas, butter, sugar, eggs, and flour until mixed.
2. Bake in a loaf pan at 350°F (175°C) for 1 hour.

Nutritional Value:

- *Calories: 220 (per serving)*
- *Protein: 3g*
- *Carbohydrates: 35g*
- *Fat: 7g*
- *Fiber: 2g*

Pureed Chocolate Chip Cookies

Prep Time: 15 minutes
Cooking Time: 10 minutes
Servings: 24 cookies

Ingredients:

- 1 cup pureed chocolate chips
- 2 cups flour
- 1/2 cup butter
- 1/2 cup sugar
- 1 egg

Instructions:

1. Mix pureed chocolate chips, butter, sugar, egg, and flour until dough forms.
2. Shape dough into cookies and bake at 375°F (190°C) for 8-10 minutes.

Nutritional Value:

- *Calories: 120 (per cookie)*
- *Protein: 2g*
- *Carbohydrates: 15g*
- *Fat: 6g*
- *Fiber: 1g*

Chapter 8: 30 Day Meal Plans

Day	Breakfast	Lunch	Dinner	Snacks
1	Pureed Oatmeal with Berries and Nuts	Pureed Carrot Soup with Grilled Cheese	Pureed Creamy Tomato Soup with Grilled Cheese	Pureed Yogurt with Fruit and Granola
2	Pureed Scrambled Eggs with Cheese	Pureed Chicken Salad Sandwich	Pureed Salmon with Roasted Vegetables	Pureed Avocado Toast
3	Pureed Yogurt Parfait	Pureed Tuna Noodle Salad	Pureed Chicken and Vegetable Curry	Smoothie
4	Smoothie	Pureed Vegetable Soup	Pureed Butternut Squash Soup with Apple	Pureed Sweet Potato Fries
5	Pureed Breakfast Bars	Pureed Pasta Salad	Pureed Chicken Noodle Soup	Pureed Applesauce
6	Pureed Avocado Toast	Pureed Beef Stew	Pureed Shepherd's Pie	Pureed Mashed Potatoes
7	Pureed Potato Pancakes	Pureed Salmon with Rice	Pureed Lentil Stew with Lemon	Pureed Hummus with Pita Bread

Day	Breakfast	Lunch	Dinner	Snacks
8	Pureed Mashed Sweet Potatoes	Pureed Chicken Stir-Fry	Pureed Salmon and Sweet Potato Mash	Pureed Carrot Sticks with Peanut Butter
9	Pureed Pumpkin Pancakes	Pureed Lentil Soup	Pureed Chicken and Rice Casserole	Pureed Rice Cakes with Apple Butter
10	Pureed Carrot Muffins	Pureed Meatloaf	Pureed Vegetable Fajitas	Pureed Cottage Cheese with Fruit
11	Pureed Yogurt Parfait	Pureed Chicken Salad Sandwich	Pureed Butternut Squash Soup with Apple	Pureed Avocado Toast
12	Pureed Scrambled Eggs with Cheese	Pureed Tuna Noodle Salad	Pureed Chicken and Vegetable Curry	Smoothie
13	Pureed Oatmeal with Berries and Nuts	Pureed Pasta Salad	Pureed Lentil Stew with Lemon	Pureed Sweet Potato Fries
14	Pureed Breakfast Bars	Pureed Beef Stew	Pureed Salmon and Sweet Potato Mash	Pureed Applesauce

Day	Breakfast	Lunch	Dinner	Snacks
15	Pureed Avocado Toast	Pureed Chicken Noodle Soup	Pureed Chicken and Rice Casserole	Pureed Mashed Potatoes
16	Pureed Potato Pancakes	Pureed Carrot Soup with Grilled Cheese	Pureed Shepherd's Pie	Pureed Hummus with Pita Bread
17	Pureed Mashed Sweet Potatoes	Pureed Salmon with Roasted Vegetables	Pureed Vegetable Fajitas	Pureed Carrot Sticks with Peanut Butter
18	Pureed Pumpkin Pancakes	Pureed Lentil Soup	Pureed Creamy Tomato Soup with Grilled Cheese	Pureed Rice Cakes with Apple Butter
19	Pureed Carrot Muffins	Pureed Meatloaf	Pureed Butternut Squash Soup with Apple	Pureed Cottage Cheese with Fruit
20	Pureed Yogurt Parfait	Pureed Chicken Stir-Fry	Pureed Chicken and Vegetable Curry	Pureed Avocado Toast
21	Smoothie	Pureed Pasta Salad	Pureed Lentil Stew with Lemon	Smoothie

Day	Breakfast	Lunch	Dinner	Snacks
22	Pureed Oatmeal with Berries and Nuts	Pureed Beef Stew	Pureed Salmon and Sweet Potato Mash	Pureed Sweet Potato Fries
23	Pureed Breakfast Bars	Pureed Carrot Soup with Grilled Cheese	Pureed Shepherd's Pie	Pureed Applesauce
24	Pureed Avocado Toast	Pureed Salmon with Rice	Pureed Chicken and Rice Casserole	Pureed Mashed Potatoes
25	Pureed Potato Pancakes	Pureed Chicken Salad Sandwich	Pureed Vegetable Fajitas	Pureed Hummus with Pita Bread
26	Pureed Mashed Sweet Potatoes	Pureed Tuna Noodle Salad	Pureed Creamy Tomato Soup with Grilled Cheese	Pureed Carrot Sticks with Peanut Butter
27	Pureed Pumpkin Pancakes	Pureed Pasta Salad	Pureed Butternut Squash Soup with Apple	Pureed Rice Cakes with Apple Butter
28	Pureed Carrot Muffins	Pureed Beef Stew	Pureed Chicken Noodle Soup	Pureed Cottage Cheese with Fruit
29	Pureed Yogurt Parfait	Pureed Lentil Soup	Pureed Shepherd's Pie	Pureed Avocado Toast
30	Smoothie	Pureed Meatloaf	Pureed Lentil Stew with Lemon	Smoothie

Recipes Index

Made in United States
Troutdale, OR
05/01/2024